Arietta

40 leichte Originalstücke
für Violoncello und Klavier

40 Easy Original Pieces
for Violoncello and Piano

40 pièces faciles originales
pour violoncello et piano

leicht / easy / facile

Herausgegeben von / Edited by / Edité par
Rainer Mohrs und / and Elmar Preusser

ED 22353
ISMN 979-0-001-15857-2

Violoncello

www.schott-music.com

Mainz · London · Berlin · Madrid · New York · Paris · Prague · Tokyo · Toronto
© 2016 SCHOTT MUSIC GmbH & Co. KG, Mainz · Printed in Germany

Inhalt / Contents

Arietta

Willem de Fesch
1687–1761

aus / from: W. de Fesch, Sonate d-Moll / D minor op. 8/3, Schott CB 54

Rigaudon I

Joseph Bodin de Boismortier
ca. 1691–1755

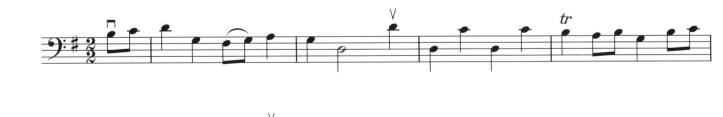

Rigaudon II

Rigaudon I da Capo

Sonata

1 Allegro

Giovanni Battista Cirri
1724–1808

aus / from: G.B. Cirri, Sonata C-Dur / C major, Schott CB 192

2 Adagio

Giovanni Battista Cirri

3 Menuetto

Giovanni Battista Cirri

Sonata
C-Dur / C major / Ut majeur
opus 40/1

Arr.: Joachim Stutschewsky
Revision: Rainer Mohrs

Jean Baptiste Bréval
1753–1823

Allegro (♩ ca. 120)

1

10

2 Rondo grazioso

Trauer
Mourning / Deuil
op. 118/2

Georg Goltermann
1824–1898

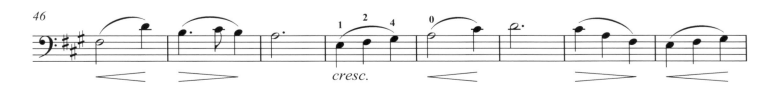

Marche funèbre
Trauermarsch / Funeral March
opus 97/2

Georg Goltermann

Lento ma non troppo

© 2016 Schott Music GmbH & Co. KG, Mainz
aus / from: G. Goltermann, Tonbilder / Musical Pictures, op. 97

Morgenspaziergang
Morning Stroll / Promenade matinale
op. 126b, No. 1

Alexander Gretchaninoff
1864–1956

aus /from: A. Gretchaninoff, In aller Frühe / Early Morning op. 126b, Schott ED 2143

Heimweh
Homesickness / Nostalgie
op. 126b, No. 2

Alexander Gretchaninoff

Spaßvogel
The Joker / Blagueur
op. 126b, No. 3

Alexander Gretchaninoff

In der Dämmerung
Twilight / Au crépuscule
op. 126b, No. 4

Alexander Gretchaninoff

Am Winterabend
On Winter's Eve / Au soir d'hiver
op. 126b, No. 6

Alexander Gretchaninoff

Burlesque
op. 126b, No. 7

Alexander Gretchaninoff

Räuber und Gendarm
Thieves and Policeman / Jeu de brigands
op. 126b, No. 9

Alexander Gretchaninoff

Walzer
Waltz / Valse
op. 126b, No. 10

Alexander Gretchaninoff

Sechs leichte Vortragsstücke
Six Easy Concert Pieces
op. 12

1 Lied / Song

Hugo Schlemüller
1872 –1918

2 Wiegenlied / Lullaby

Hugo Schlemüller

3 Scherzo

Hugo Schlemüller

4 Ländler / Landler

Hugo Schlemüller

5 Marsch / March

Hugo Schlemüller

6 Gebet / Prayer

Hugo Schlemüller

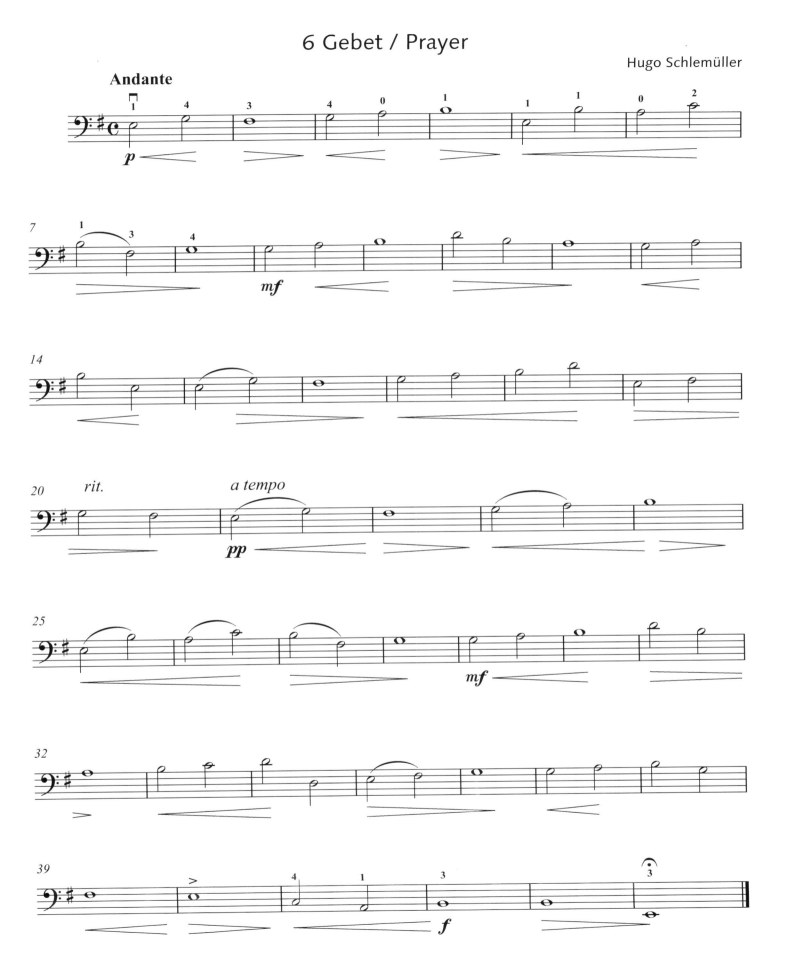

Sechs leichte Vortragsstücke
Six Easy Concert Pieces
op. 4

1 Melodie

Arnold Trowell
1887–1966

2 Idylle

Arnold Trowell

3 Chanson sans paroles

Arnold Trowell

4 Menuet

Tempo di Menuetto

Arnold Trowell

5 Gavotte

Arnold Trowell

Tempo di Gavotte

6 Petite marche

Arnold Trowell

In Steady March Time (♪ = 144)

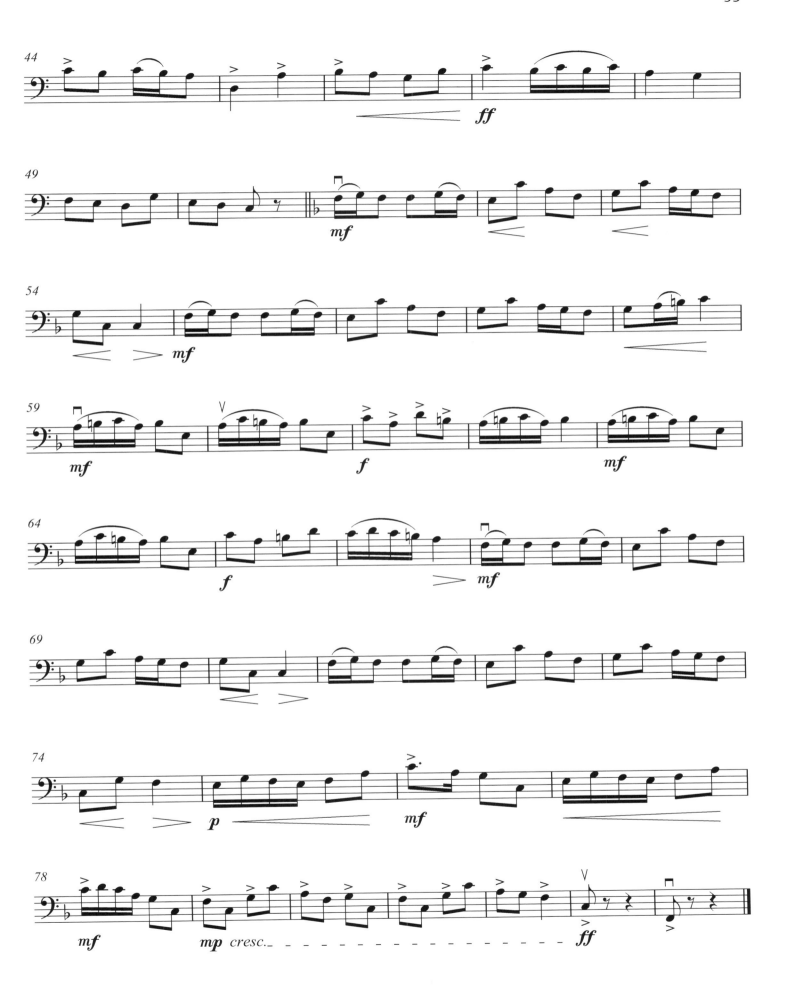

Drei leichte Stücke
Three Easy Pieces

1

Mäßig schnell, munter (♩ = 92)

Paul Hindemith
1895–1963

aus / from: P. Hindemith, Drei leichte Stücke / Three Easy Pieces, Schott ED 2771

2

Paul Hindemith

3

Paul Hindemith

Lebhaft (♩. ca. 76)

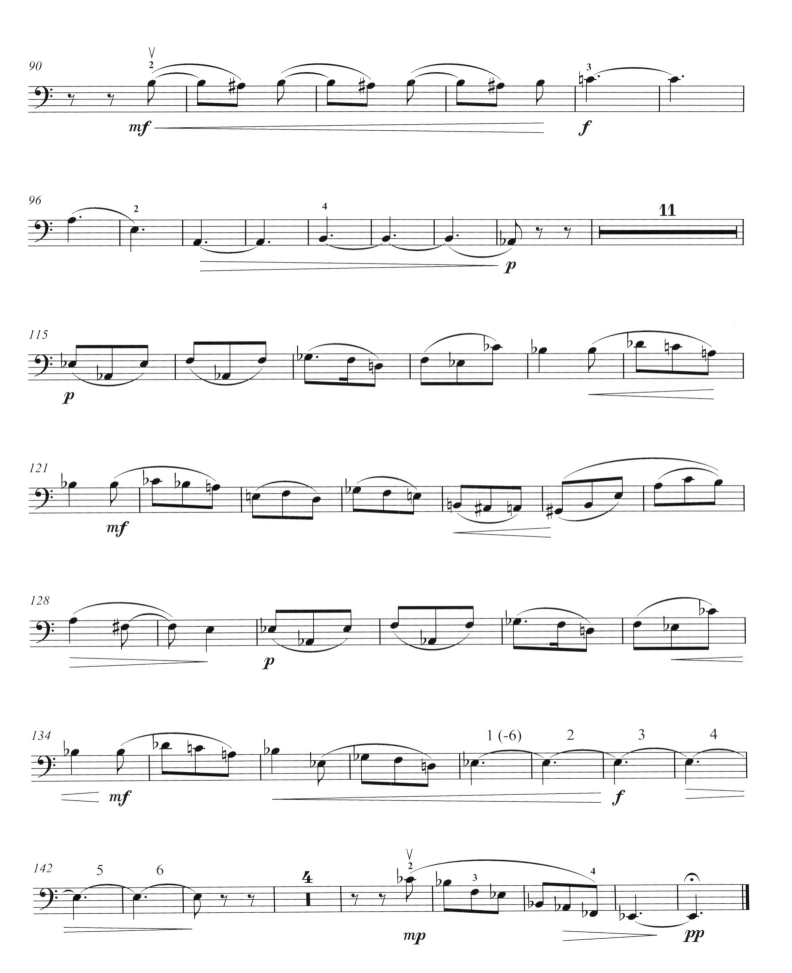

Serenade

Marie Dare
1902–1976

Aus wendetechnischen Gründen bleibt diese Seite frei.
This page is left blank to save an unnecessary page turn.

Valse in G

Marie Dare

3 Short Stories
Prelude

Eduard Pütz
1911–2000

aus / from: E. Pütz, Short Stories, 10 Easy Pieces for Violoncello and Piano, Schott ED 7533

Sunny Morning

Singing ♩ ca. 66

Eduard Pütz

Stomping Boys
(Blues)

Eduard Pütz

Disco Hit

Gabriel Koeppen
*1958

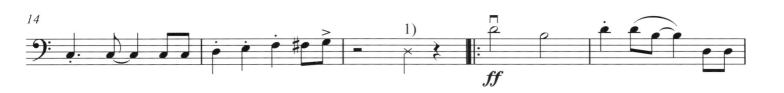

1) „Bassdrum": Der Cellist schlägt mit der linken flachen Hand auf die Decke.
   Der Pianist klatscht oder schlägt auf einen bassig klingenden Teil des Klavieres,
   z.B. von unten gegen den Tastenkasten.
   'Bass drum': The cellist slaps the top of the cello with the flat of his left hand.
   The pianist slaps or hits a deep sounding part of the piano, e.g. the bottom side of the keyboard.

2) Cellist: Glissando in beliebiger Tonhöhe und/oder hoher Ruf auf „Huh".
   Pianist: Klatschen und/oder hoher Ruf auf „Huh".
   Cellist: glissando in any pitch and/or shouting 'hoo' in a high voice.
   Pianist: clapping and/or shouting 'hoo' in a high voice.

In memoriam Willem de Fesch

Arietta 2015

Rainer Mohrs
*1953

Slow Waltz